of Thomas Raybank And also of all those Messuages Cottages or other
of said Richard William Pain Richard Curtis and John Raybank and of all ways lights Easements and
singular the said premises herein before mentioned belonging or in any wise appertaining The whole of
own and Elizabeth his wife (both now deceased) of and from John Banford the younger and Elizabeth his
of the said Thomas Brown unto the only use and behoof of the said Thomas Brown and Thomas
the said will and Estate out of the said Thomas Brown deceased (after his said wife's decease) unto his son John
of the said unto his Brothers the said Francis Brown and John Brown deceased and their several heirs
Francis Brown and John Brown party hereto are by virtue of the said devise Brown seized of the several
Brown hath her power in the said undivided Moiety or half part thereof hereby conveyed) And of the other
premises herein before mentioned and every part thereof with the appurtenants And also all the Estate
interest whatsoever of them the said Mary Brown and John Brown party hereto in and to the same together with all
any part thereof now in the hands custody or power of the said Mary Brown and John Brown party hereto
use or equity To have and to hold the said undivided Moiety or half part of the said several Messuages
ments unto the said Francis Brown his heirs and assigns to the only proper use and behoof of the said
premises herein before mentioned and every part thereof with the appurtenants Due and of right appertaining
Administrators both covenant promise and grant to and with the said Francis Brown his heirs and
Mary Browne and John Browne party hereto to do are the true and lawful owners of the said undivided
hereto is the true of forego in his own right of a good and pure absolute and indefeasible Estate of Inheritance
or other lawful matter or thing to alter charge determine defeat or make void the same And also that
loves good right full power and absolute lawful and absolute Authority to grant bargain sell alien release and
in his heirs and assigns to his and their only proper use and behoof as aforesaid And further that
one and at all times forever hereafter peaceably and quietly have hold use occupy possess and enjoy the
without any Let Trouble Eviction or Molestation Interruption or Denial of them the said Mary Brown
or Assigns freed and discharged or otherwise well and sufficiently saved harmless and kept indemnified by the said
and against all former and other gifts grants Bargains Sales Leases Mortgages Jointures Dowers Wills
obligatory Statutes Merchant and of the Staple Recognizances Judgments Executions Extents and
and Incumbrances whatsoever had made done committed or suffered or to be had made committed done

Quod cū audisset dauid: descendit in presidiū. Philistijm autem venientes diffusli sunt in valle raphaim. Et cō= suluit dauid dūm dicens. Si ascendā ad philistijm· et si dabis eos ī manu mea? Et dixit dūs ad dauid. Ascende: qa tradens dabo philistijm in manu tua. Venit ergo dauid ad baalphara= sim: et percussit eos ibi et dixit. Diuisit dūs inimicos meos corā me: sicut di= uident aque. Propterea vocatū e no= men loci illi9 baalpharasim. Et reliq= runt ibi sculptilia sua: q tulit dauid et viri eo. Et addiderunt adhuc philisti= im ut ascenderent: et diffussi sūt ī valle raphaim. Cōsuluit autē dauid dūm. Si ascendā cōtra philisteos: z tradas eos in manus meas? Qui rūdit. Nō ascendas cōtra eos sed gira post tergū corū: z venies ad eos ex aduso pirorū. Et cū audieris sonitū clamoris gra= dietis ī cacumie piroz tūc imbis pliū: qa tūc egredietē dūs āte faciē tuā: ut p

Sappi lettor digniſſimo, che le lettere cancellareſche ſono de diuerſe qualita di corpi, aſte, legature, & incatenature, torture, dritte tonde & nõ tonde, trattizate & ſenza tratti, & altri ſentimēti de altre nature come hai potuto uedere nelle ſcritte qualita de lettere, le quali ſi uſano nelle cancellarie de tutte le cita della Italia, & doue ſi coſtuma una qualita, e doue una tra, Ma p& dar buon principio al noſtro inſegnare a ſcriuere, nui principiaremo da quelle che ſono piu biſognoſe & neceſſarie uniuerſalmēte a ognuno cioe quelle che piu ſe coſtumano al preſente in diuerſe cancellarie, & maxime in quella del ſereniſſimo dominio Venetiano dal quale gia molti anni fui & ſono prouiſionato per merito di queſta uirtute, & coſi a queſte qualita de lettere cancellareſche daremo bono principio e prima.

Concioſia coſa diſcreto lettore che allo amaeſtramēto de inſegnare a ſcriuere le ſopraſcrite qualita de lettere io te poteria dire (&)u doueſti imparare prima gli alphabeti et poi gli uerſi, con la uirtu della tua prudentia, praticando et retrahendo gli mei eſempli in breui giorni ti potreſti fare eccellente ſcrittore, de quelle qualita de lettere cancellareſche, ouer de altra qualita che uorrai imparare, ma per maggiore tua dilucidationi & accio che con maggiore preſtezza di tempo, tu poſſi imparare io qui ſeguente ti daro la ragioue con li ſecreti & maeſtreuoli modi, a lettera per lettera, et poi anchora ti daro la ragione della legatura, & incatenatura, di tutti gli nomi, con larte di la geometria,

Onſiderando adongue in queſto noſtro primo amaeſtramento, ſapi come tutte le lettere dello alphabeto cãcellareſcho enſeno da queſto ſottoſcritto quadro biſlongo come ſeguendo piu chiaramente intenderai.

&per dartil o ſecondo amaeſtramēto ſapi che uolendo imparare la preditta lettera cancellareſcha, prima el te biſogna imparare tutte le lettere dello alphabeto ſu le rige, & poi quando ſaperai ſcriuere, ſcriuerai ſenza riga per fino (&) la mano hauera compreſa la ſua perfettione, le quale letterie dello alphabeto imparai a fare prima queſto ſottoſcritto corpo ilquale enſe del gudãro biſlongo, et penden

te ſi come qui di ſotto tu uedi lo eſempio.

ADungue a queſta altra conſideratione ſapi che queſto ſopraſcritto corpo fatto con la ſua miſura et arte, preſto preſto adoperando col tuo ingegno per arte de la geometria trazerai queſte ſottoſcritte tre lettere, le guale te ſcriuo qui di ſotto per tuo eſempio.

La ſopradetta lettera a, ſe trazze del ſopraſcritto corpo in queſto modo, prima tirerai una gamba ritta che ſia uno poco pendente a canto del ditto corpo in tal modo c he la maggior parte del ditto corpo rimanga ſerrato, & in ultimo della preditta gamba daragli uno poco di garbetto, ilquale garbetto ſi chiama una laſſata perche la laſſi, per che il ſuo finimento ſi come qui di ſotto tu uedi lo eſempio, per tuo amaeſtramento.

La lettera, b, ſi trazze pur del quadro, & ſi tira prima una aſta uina & galiarda laquale habbia uno poco di dependentia, ſi come feſti alla lettera a, con uno punto fermo & pēdente, nel ſuo principio in forma de uno punto nel princi

pio de laſta & poi quando ſerai in capo de laſta a canto la riga ritornerai in ſu per la medeſima haſſa in tal modo che tu poſſi fabricare il corpo della lettera a, alla rouerſa & ſara fabricata la tua lettera, b, ma fagli romagnire lo ſuo corpo, uno poco aperto ſi come feſti alla lettera, a, come tu uedi lo ſottoſcritto exempio.

La lettera c, ſi trazze del quadro biſlongo ſi come feſti nēl corpo della lettera a, ma ben el ſi tira in doi tratti e prima tu hai a tirar uno mezo corpo della lettera a, et poi tu ha-uerai a pigliare la ultima extremita di ſopra del ditto mezo corpo, & farai uno ponto che uengi tondizãdo, allo camino come ſe tu uoleſti chiudere per fare la lettera o, in doi tratti ſi come tu uedi lo ſottoſcritto exempio.

La lettera d, farai come feſti la lettera a, & cõ laſta della lettera b, come tu uedi lo ſottoſcritto exempio.

La lettera e, la farai ſi come tu feſti la lettera c, a pūto eccetto quando tirarai lo punto di ſopra della lettera c, intrarai

Le lettere cancellaresche sopranominate se fanno tonde
longe large tratizate e non tratizate ET per che io
to scritto questa variacione de lettera la qual im=
pareraj secundo li nostri precetti et opere

A aa b.c.d.ee.f.g.h.i.k.l.m.n.o.p.q.r.s.t.u.x.y.z.&

Le lettere cancellaresche sopranominate se fanno tonde
longe large tratizate e non tratizate ET per che io
to scritto questa variacione de lettera la qual im=
pareraj secundo li nostri precetti et opere

A aa b.c.d.ee.f.g.h.i.k.l.m.n.o.p.q.r.s.t.u.x.y.z.&

Le lettere cancellaresche sopranominate se fanno tonde
longe large tratizate e non tratizate ET per che io
to scritto questa variacione de lettera la qual im=
pareraj secundo li nostri precetti et opere

A aa b.c.d.ee.f.g.h.i.k.l.m.n.o.p.q.r.s.t.u.x.y.z.&

Le lettere cancellaresche sopranominate se fanno tonde
longe large tratizate e non tratizate ET per che io
to scritto questa variacione de lettera la qual im=
pareraj secundo li nostri precetti et opere

A aa b.c.d.ee.f.g.h.i.k.l.m.n.o.p.q.r.s.t.u.x.y.z.&

Le lettere cancellaresche sopranominate se fanno tonde
longe large tratizate e non tratizate ET per che io
to scritto questa variacione de lettera la qual im=
pareraj secundo li nostri precetti et opere

A aa b.c.d.ee.f.g.h.i.k.l.m.n.o.p.q.r.s.t.u.x.y.z.&

Le lettere cancellaresche sopranominate se fanno tonde
longe large tratizate e non tratizate ET per che io
to scritto questa variacione de lettera la qual im=
pareraj secundo li nostri precetti et opere

A aa b.c.d.ee.f.g.h.i.k.l.m.n.o.p.q.r.s.t.u.x.y.z.&

and Conveniences therewith connected, to be called the "Edinburgh & Bathga...
...nce at a point on the Edinburgh and Glasgow Railway, at or near to the Rai...
...Parish of Ratho, and County of Edinburgh, or in that part of the Parish of ...
...e said County of Edinburgh, or one or other of them, and to terminate, within, at, o...
...rgh of Bathgate, in the Parish of Bathgate, and County of Linlithgow, by a ju...
...ndon Railway from Airdrie to Bathgate, or otherways. Together also with...
...ways, with all proper Works and Conveniences therewith connected, viz. First, A Br...
...om the said intended Main Line of Railway, at or near to the Lands or Farm ...
...of the Parish of Kirkliston situated within the County of Edinburgh, or at or...
...s of Elliston or Illiston, situated in the Parish of Uphall, and County of ...
...rt of the Parish of Kirkliston situated within the said County of Linlithgow...
...ar to the Town or Village of Mid Calder, in the Parish of Mid Calder, & Cou...
...point betwixt the Towns or Villages of Mid Calder and East Calder, in the ...
...ed Parishes of Kirknewton and East Calder, in the County of Edinburgh; Seco...
...to diverge from the said intended Main Line of Railway, at or near to the Fa...
...nd Parish of Uphall and County of Linlithgow, to the Freestone Quarries of t...
...n the said Parish of Linlithgow, and partly within the said Parish of U...
...nty of Linlithgow; Third, A Branch Railway to diverge from the said intended M...
...e a point at or near to the Lands or Farm of Barracks, in the Parish of Livings...
...thgow aforesaid, or from a point at or near to the Farm of Tailend, in the Pa...
...Farm of Deans, in the said Parish of Bathgate, and County of Linlithgow, and...
...t at, in, or near to the Village of Whitburn, in the Parish of Whitburn, & Coun...
...id. Fourth, A Branch Railway from or near to the point at which the said ...
...f Railway will terminate at Bathgate aforesaid, to, or near to the point at whic...
...lway to Whitburn will terminate at Whitburn aforesaid, with a connecting Li...
...med Branch Line to the Village of Blackburn in the Parish of Livingstone a...
...ther Connecting Line from said Branch Railway to Whitburn, from a point a...
...Moss-side, to another point on the said intended Main Line, at or near to the L...
...ng Grove, all in the Parish of Bathgate, and County of Linlithgow aforesaid;
...d, or some of them, all as shewn on the Plan aftermentioned, or some parts or porti...
...Railways and Branches, and that the Property mentioned in the annexed Sch...
...n which I understand you are interested, as therein stated, will be required for ...
...Undertaking according to the lines thereof, as at present laid out, or may be requi...
...e usual powers of deviation, to the usual extent of One Hundred Yards on either si...
...the extent of the limit of deviation delineated on the plans aftermentioned, which ...
...the said Act, and will be passed through, in the manner mentioned in such Sche...
...I also beg to inform you, that a Plan and Section of the said Undertaking, with a Boo...
...deposited in the Office in Edinburgh of the principal Sheriff Clerk of the Cou... by ...
...Office in Linlithgow of the principal Sheriff Clerk of the County of Linlithgow, on the ...
...and that Copies of the said Plan and Section, with a Book of Reference thereto, will ...
...pection with the Schoolmaster, if any, and if there be no Schoolmaster, with the Sess...
...which your Property is situate, and with the Town Clerk of the Town or Burgh of B...
...day of December instant, on which Plans your Property is designated by the numbers b...
...chedule. As I am required to report to Parliament, whether you assent to or dissen...
...rtaking, or whether you are neuter in respect thereto, you will oblige me by wri...
...nt, dissent, or neutrality, in the form left herewith, and returning the same to me, wit...
...fore the 8th day of January next, and if there should be any error or misdescription ...

and Conveniences therewith connected, to be called the "Edinburgh & Bathgat
...ce at a point on the Edinburgh and Glasgow Railway, at or near to the Rat...
...Parish of Ratho and County of Edinburgh, or in that part of the Parish of K...
...said County of Edinburgh, or one or other of them, and to terminate within, at, or...
...rgh of Bathgate, in the Parish of Bathgate, and County of Linlithgow, by a jun...
...index Railway from Airdrie to Bathgate, or otherways, Together also with...
...ways, with all proper Works and Conveniences therewith connected, viz: First, A Bra...
...in the said intended Main Line of Railway, at or near to the Lands or Farm...
...of the Parish of Kirkliston, situated within the County of Edinburgh, or at or...
...of Elliston or Illiston, situated in the Parish of Uphall, and County of L...
...rt of the Parish of Kirkliston situated within the said County of Linlithgow...
...r to the Town or Village of Mid Calder, in the Parish of Mid Calder, & Coun...
...point betwixt the Towns or Villages of Mid Calder and East Calder, in the...
...ed Parishes of Kirknewton and East Calder, in the County of Edinburgh; Secon...
...to diverge from the said intended Main Line of Railway, at or near to the Fa...
...d Parish of Uphall and County of Linlithgow, to the Freestone Quarries of B...
...the said Parish of Linlithgow, and partly within the said Parish of Up...
...rty of Linlithgow; Third, A Branch Railway to diverge from the said intended M...
...a point at or near to the Lands or Farm of Barrucks, in the Parish of Livings...
...hgow aforesaid, or from a point at or near to the Farm of Tailend, in the Par...
...Farm of Deans, in the said Parish of Bathgate, and County of Linlithgow, and...
...at, in, or near to the Village of Whitburn, in the Parish of Whitburn, & Coun...
...d: Fourth, A Branch Railway from or near to the point at which the said in...
...l Railway will terminate at Bathgate aforesaid, to, or near to the point at which...
...way to Whitburn will terminate at Whitburn aforesaid, with a connecting Lin...
...nes Branch Line to the Village of Blackburn, in the Parish of Livingstone afo...
...ther Connecting Line from said Branch Railway to Whitburn, from a point at...
...Moss-side, to another point on the said intended Main Line, at or near to the La...
...y Grove, all in the Parish of Bathgate, and County of Linlithgow aforesaid;...
...d, or some of them, all as shewn on the Plan aftermentioned, or some parts or portio...
...Railways and Branches, and that the Property mentioned in the annexed Sche...
...w which I understand you are interested, as therein stated, will be required for t...
...Undertaking according to the lines thereof, as at present laid out or may be requi...
...usual powers of deviation, to the usual extent of One Hundred Yards on either si...
...the extent of the limit of deviation delineated on the plans aftermentioned, which...
...the said Act, and will be passed through, in the manner mentioned in such Sched...
...also beg to inform you, that a Plan and Section of the said Undertaking, with a Book...
...deposited in the Office in Edinburgh of the principal Sheriff Clerk of the Coun by...
...ffice in Linlithgow of the principal Sheriff Clerk of the County of Linlithgow, on the...
...and that Copies of the said Plan and Section, with a Book of Reference thereto, will...
...pection with the Schoolmaster, if any, and if there be no Schoolmaster, with the Sessio...
...which your Property is situate, and with the Town Clerk of the Town or Burgh of B...
...day of December instant, on which Plans your Property is designated by the numbers s...
...hedule. As I am required to report to Parliament, whether you assent to or dissen...
...taking, or whether you are neuter in respect thereto, you will oblige me by writ...
...t dissent, or neutrality, in the form left herewith, and returning the same to me, wit...
...fore the 5th day of January next, and if there should be any error or missdescription...

Je n'ai pas à te donner
le motif de mon retard à
t'écrire, n'est-ce pas ? puisque
tu as appris mon accident.
Ma jambe était prise sous l'échelle
et par le choc j'ai eu les chairs
meurtries, la cheville, le pied
très enflés et tout noirs. Je suis
restée au lit une dizaine de
jours, ne pouvant appuyer mon
pied ; puis j'ai commencé à
me lever quelques heures ayant

se mariera-t-elle à l'église
aussi ! Et c'est pour le mois
de juin, on devra bientôt faire
commencer les préparatifs.

Tu me dis que le vieux château
est en vente, c'est le Barry sans
doute métairie du bourg, Bel
et Brouillets. Alors M. Jacques
ne veut rien conserver à
Clermont. Y aura-t-il des
acquéreurs ?

La Mouline est revenue alors
aux anciens propriétaires.
La femme Nadom doit être en
effet contente de rester là, mais
le prix de vente n'égale pas le
prix d'achat. Encore s'il lui
reste un peu quelque chose

St Cyr, 29 avril 1934

Ma chère Amélia,

me chercher. La lettre
s'est croisée avec celle
nous attendons leur
Nous te chargeons,
Aline et moi d'offrir
amitiés à Mme Gélas, à
Louise, Cher Moïse et à t
naissances.

Pour toi, nos plus a
toujours la jambe a
Maintenant je ma
mais les nerfs sont
je ne double pas fa
le pied. Enfin puis
du mieux, il faut
les mouvements re
leur élasticité. Aline m
recommandé de ne
à l'échelle, j'ai déso
été bien punie.

Je te remercie m
Amélia de tous les
que tu me donnes
Vous avez été tém
beau mariage de
c'est extraordinaire
Clermont. Et Mlle

Vos indésirables sou
Vous allez faire un
ce joli là. Le boi
prendra son calme
pas besoin de gen
mettre la paix. Je
être bien débarras

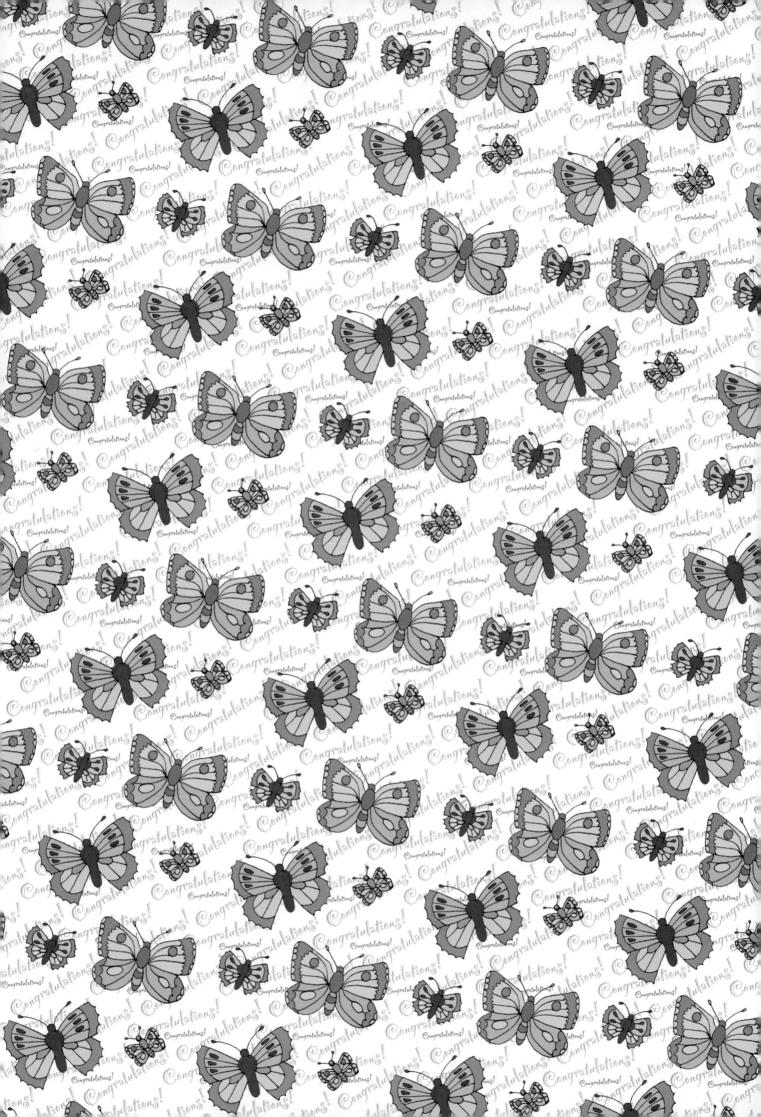

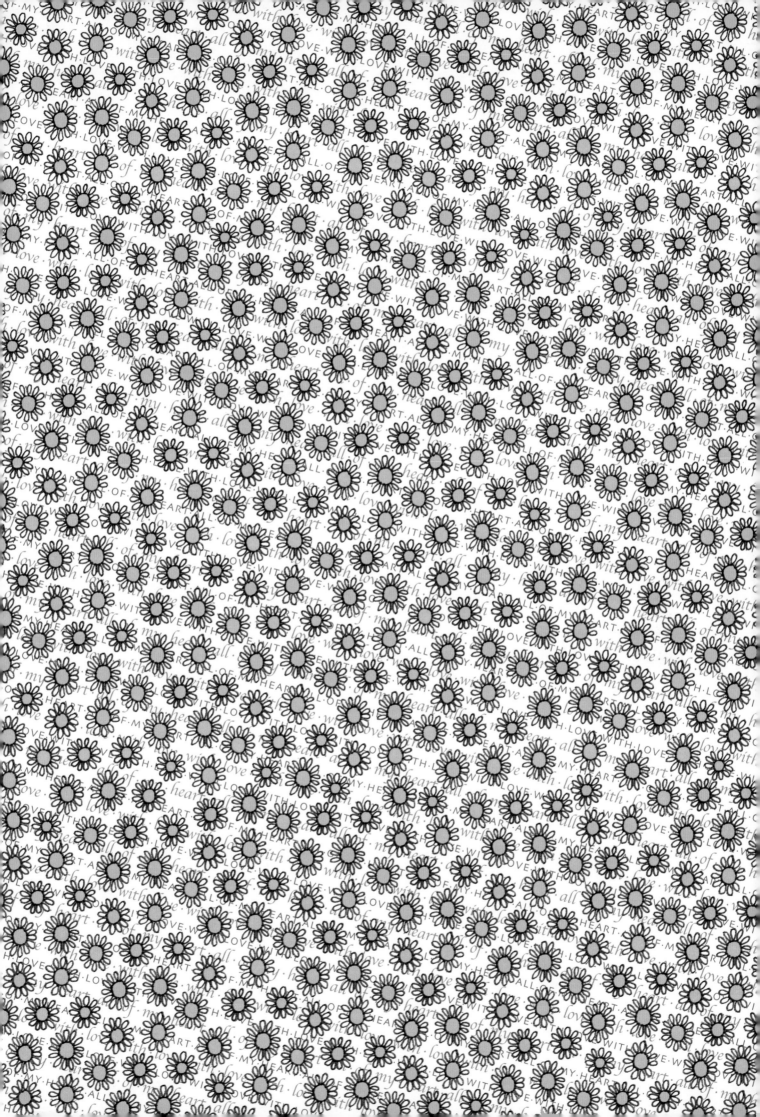

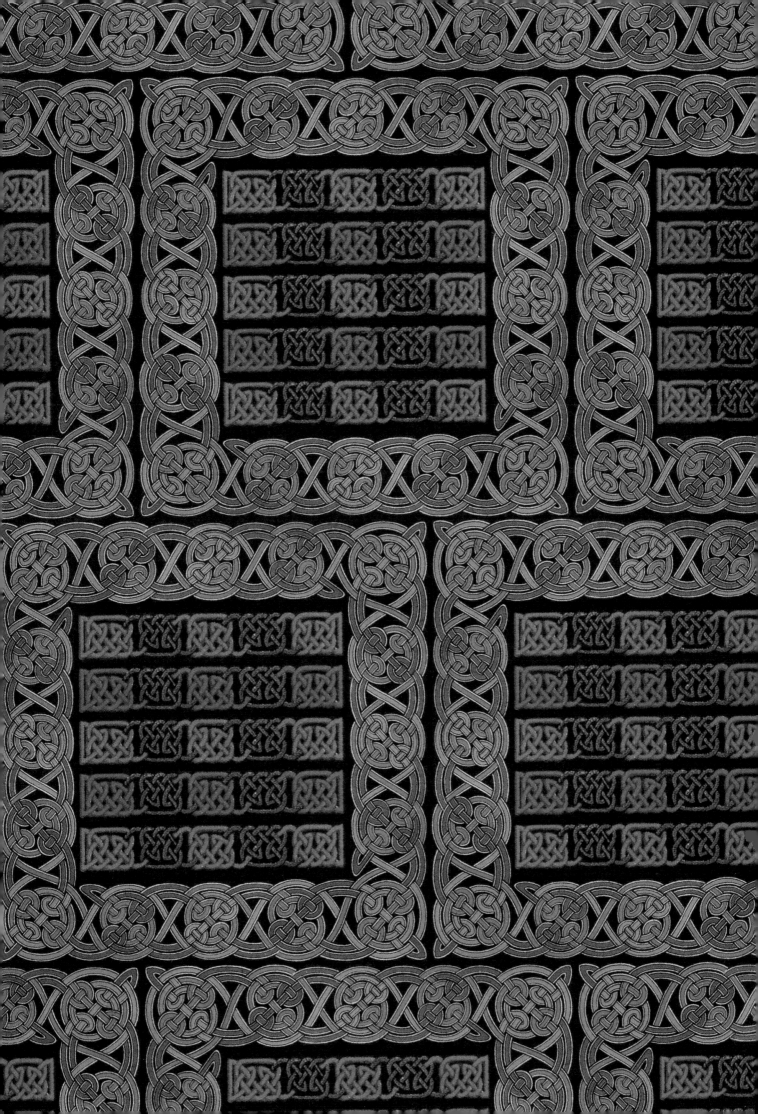

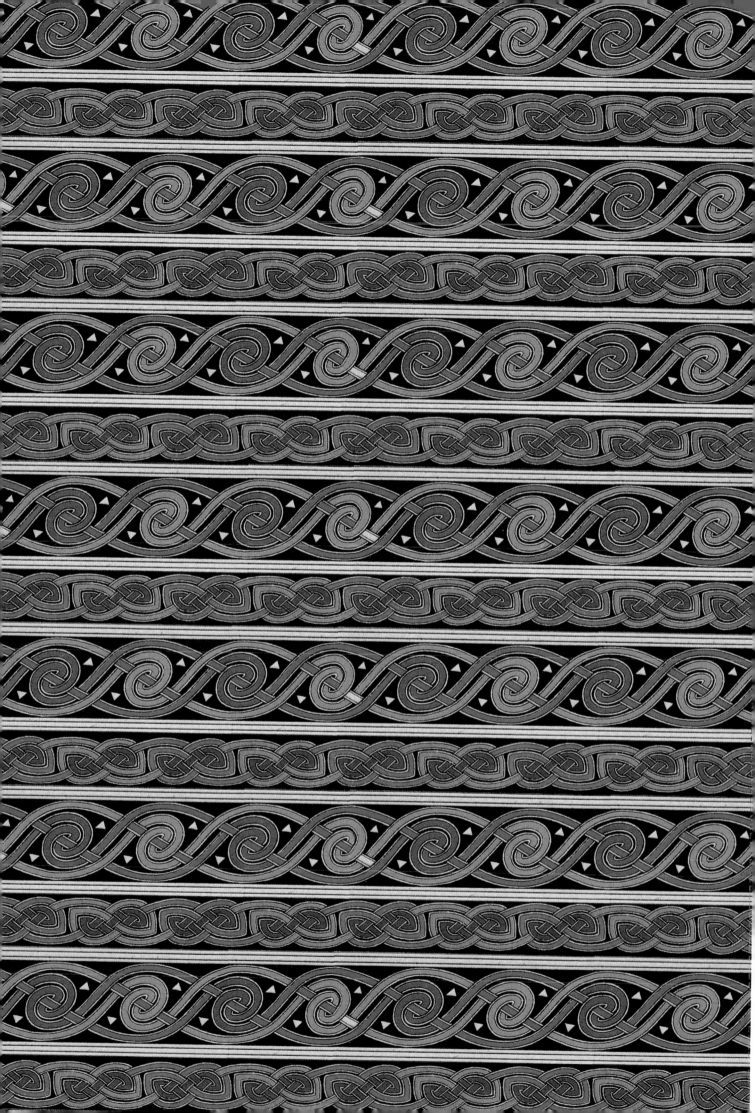

ÉIREANN GO BRÁCH · ÉIREANN GO BRÁCH · É
IRELAND FOREVER · IRELAND FOREVER

ÉIREANN GO BRÁCH · ÉIREANN GO BRÁCH · ÉIREA
EVER · IRELAND FOREVER · IRELAND FOREVER · IR

EANN GO BRÁCH · ÉIREANN GO BRÁCH · ÉIREANN G
IRELAND FOREVER · IRELAND FOREVER · IRELAN

GO BRÁCH · ÉIREANN GO BRÁCH · ÉIREANN GO BR
LAND FOREVER · IRELAND FOREVER · IRELAND FO

RÁCH · ÉIREANN GO BRÁCH · ÉIREANN GO BRÁCH
FOREVER · IRELAND FOREVER · IRELAND FOREVE

D · ÉIREANN GO BRÁCH · ÉIREANN GO BRÁCH · ÉIR
EVER · IRELAND FOREVER · IRELAND FOREVER · I

REANN GO BRÁCH · ÉIREANN GO BRÁCH · ÉIREANN
· IRELAND FOREVER · IRELAND FOREVER · IRELA

N GO BRÁCH · ÉIREANN GO BRÁCH · ÉIREANN GO
LAND FOREVER · IRELAND FOREVER · IRELAND F

ÁCH · ÉIREANN GO BRÁCH · ÉIREANN GO BRÁCH
FOREVER · IRELAND FOREVER · IRELAND FOREVE

ÉIREANN GO BRÁCH · ÉIREANN GO BRÁCH · ÉIRE
EVER · IRELAND FOREVER · IRELAND FOREVER · I

EANN GO BRÁCH · ÉIREANN GO BRÁCH · ÉIREANN
IRELAND FOREVER · IRELAND FOREVER · IREL

GO BRÁCH · ÉIREANN GO BRÁCH · ÉIREANN GO B
LAND FOREVER · IRELAND FOREVER · IRELAND FO

BRÁCH · ÉIREANN GO BRÁCH · ÉIREANN GO BRÁCH
D FOREVER · IRELAND FOREVER · IRELAND FOREV

...oí · a chuisle mo choí · a chuisle mo choí · a
...lse of my heart · pulse of my heart · pulse

a chuisle mo choí · a chuisle mo choí · a chu
of my heart · pulse of my heart · pulse of

...uisle mo choí · a chuisle mo choí · a chuisle
...y heart · pulse of my heart · pulse of my he

...mo choí · a chuisle mo choí · a chuisle mo c
art · pulse of my heart · pulse of my heart

choí · a chuisle mo choí · a chuisle mo choí
pulse of my heart · pulse of my heart · pu

· a chuisle mo choí · a chuisle mo choí · a ch
...se of my heart · pulse of my heart · pulse o

...huisle mo choí · a chuisle mo choí · a chuisl
...my heart · pulse of my heart · pulse of my

...le mo choí · a chuisle mo choí · a chuisle mo
heart · pulse of my heart · pulse of my hea

...oí · a chuisle mo choí · a chuisle mo choí · a
...lse of my heart · pulse of my heart · pulse

a chuisle mo choí · a chuisle mo choí · a chu
of my heart · pulse of my heart · pulse of

...uisle mo choí · a chuisle mo choí · a chuisle
y heart · pulse of my heart · pulse of my he

...mo choí · a chuisle mo choí · a chuisle mo c
art · pulse of my heart · pulse of my heart

choí · a chuisle mo choí · a chuisle mo choí
pulse of my heart · pulse of my heart · pu

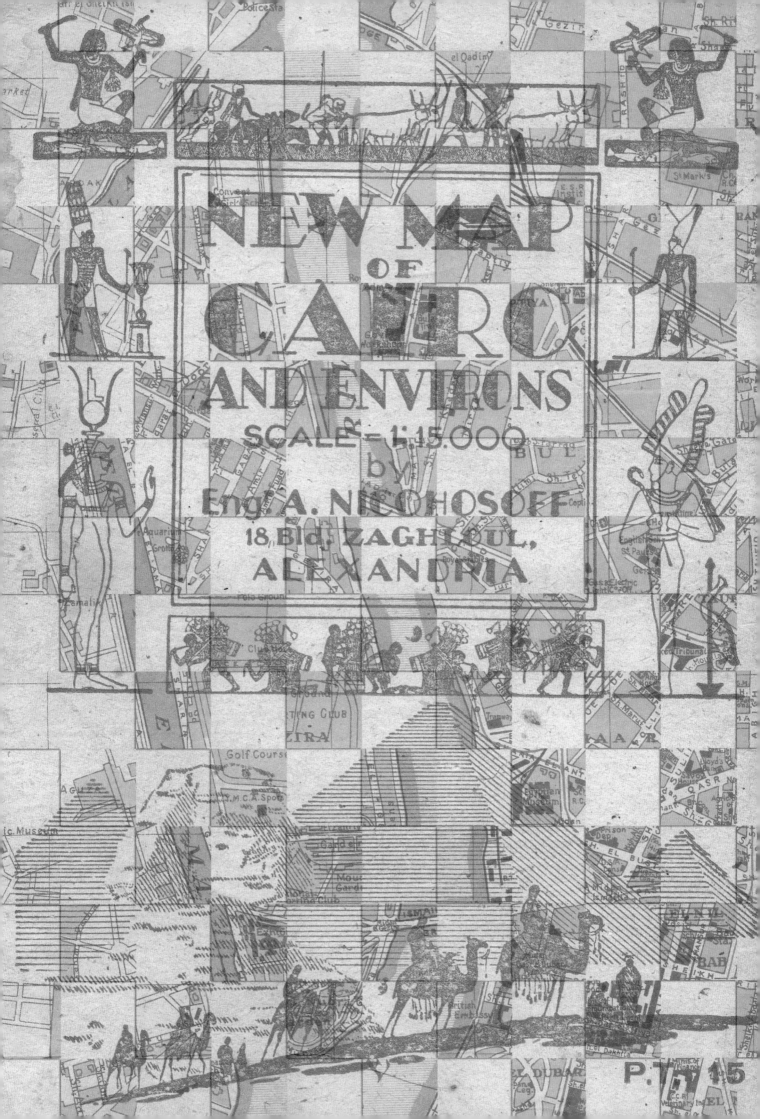

NEW MAP
OF
CAIRO
AND ENVIRONS
SCALE = 1:15.000
by
Eng. A. NICOHOSOFF
18 Bld. ZAGHLOUL,
ALEXANDRIA

P.T. 15

M.G. TWO-LITRE SALOON

ASTON MARTIN
FOUR-SEATER TOURER

ROLLS-ROYCE PHA

RILEY TWO-LITRE
RACING MODEL

FRAZER NASH
SHELSLEY TWO-SEATER

ALFA-ROMEO

A.C. SPORTS TWO-SEATER

BUGATTI 3·3 LITRE

SINGER 1½-LITRE
LE MANS TWO-SEATER

MASERATI

SS JAGUAR 2½-LITRE SALOON

PHANTOM III

E.R.A 1½-LITRE

MERCÉDÈS-BENZ

BRITISH SALMSON 20-90 SPORTS TWO-SE

M.G. MAGNETTE N TYPE

ALVIS SPEED 20 DROP-HEAD COUPÉ

AUTO-UNION

M.G. TWO-LITRE SALOON

ASTON MARTIN
FOUR-SEATER TOURER

ROLLS-ROYCE PHA

RILEY TWO-LITRE
RACING MODEL

FRAZER NASH
SHELSLEY TWO-SEATER

ALFA-ROMEO

A.C. SPORTS TWO-SEATER

BUGATTI 3·3 LITRE

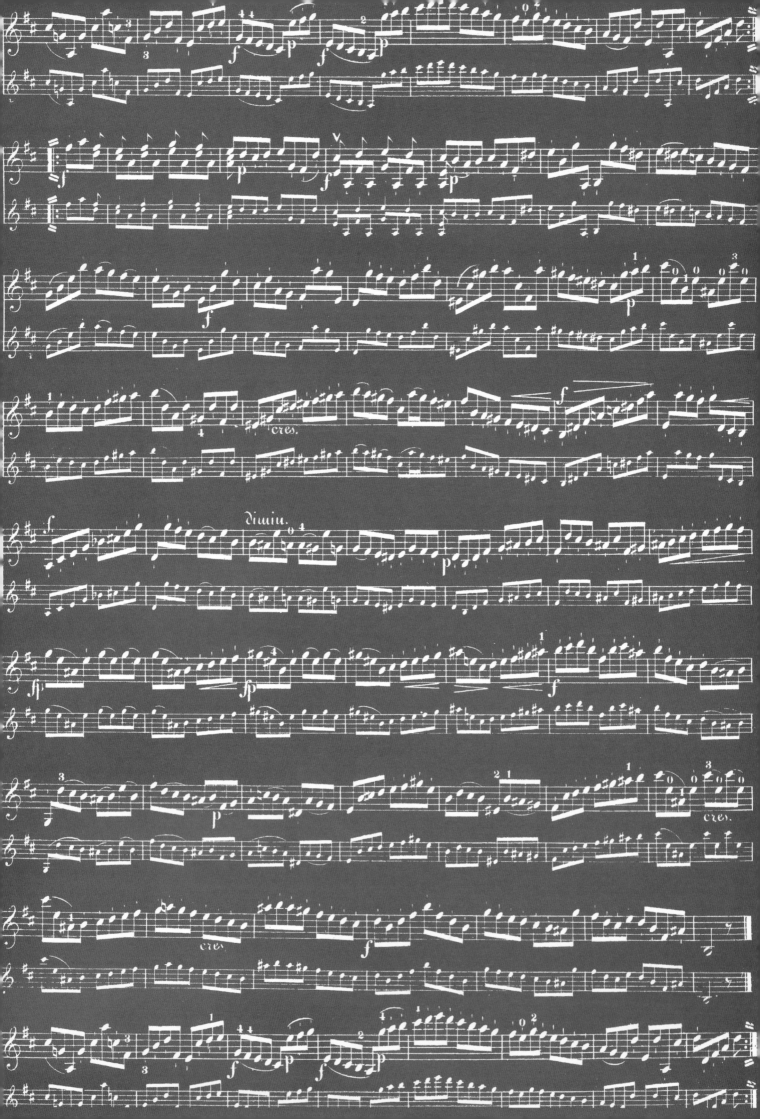

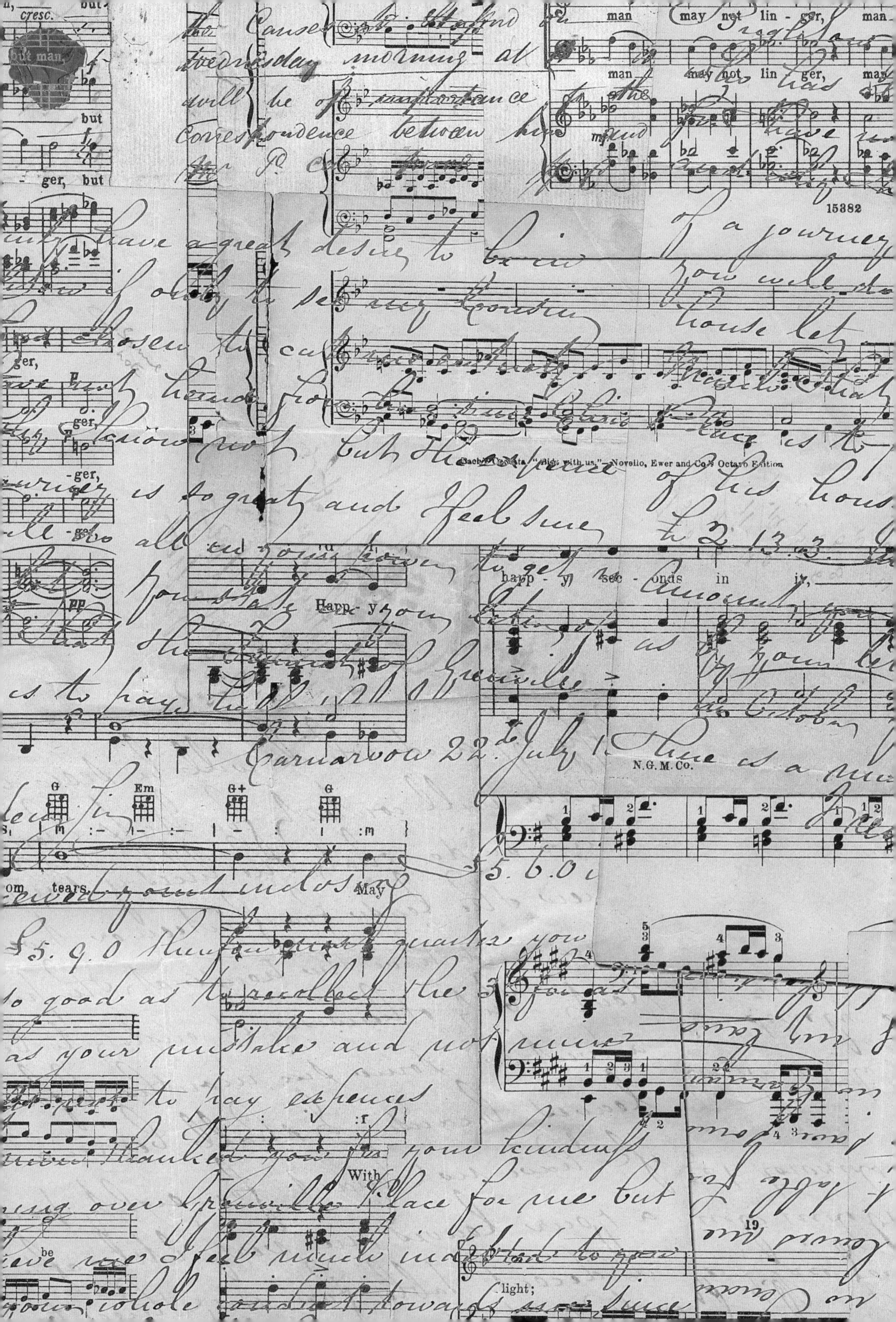

cresc.
but
but
ger, but
man
may not lin - ger, man
man may not lin ger, man
15382
Bach's Cantata, "Bide with us." – Novello, Ewer and Co.'s Octavo Edition
Happ - y
happ - y sec - onds in it,
N.G.M.Co.
G
Em
G+
G
tears.
May
With
19
light;
Carnarvon 22d July

Rob. Schumann's

WERKE

für Pianoforte solo

revidirt von

ALFRED DÖRFFEL

mit Fingersatz versehen von

RICHARD SCHMIDT

Album für die Jugend, Op. 68.

Kinderscenen, Op. 15.

LEIPZIG
C. F. PETERS

一節 一節二
二葉二
渾然一片
還瓏蕉
軾文同鄭燮

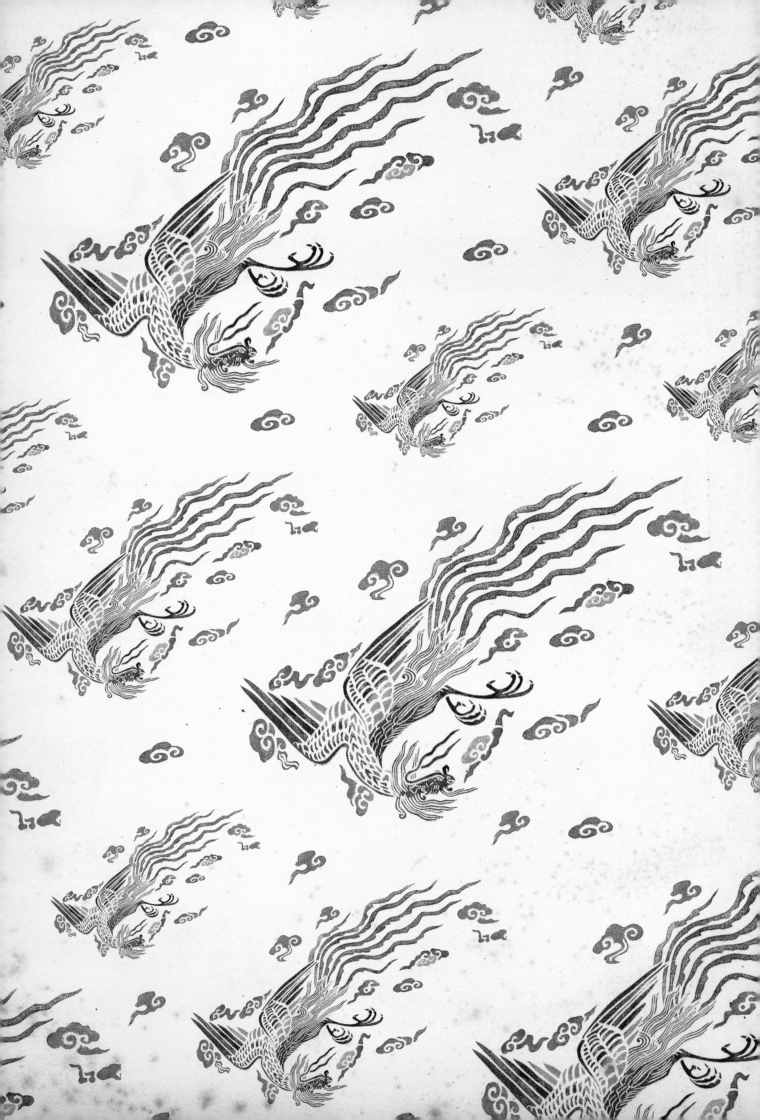

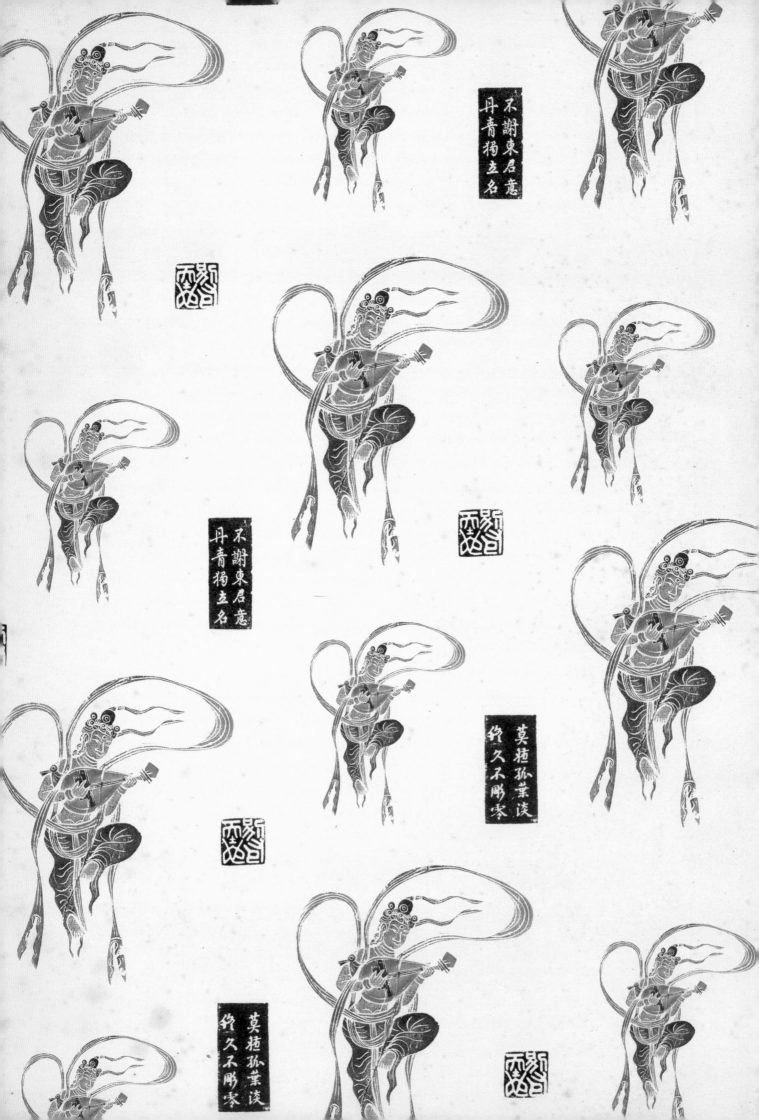

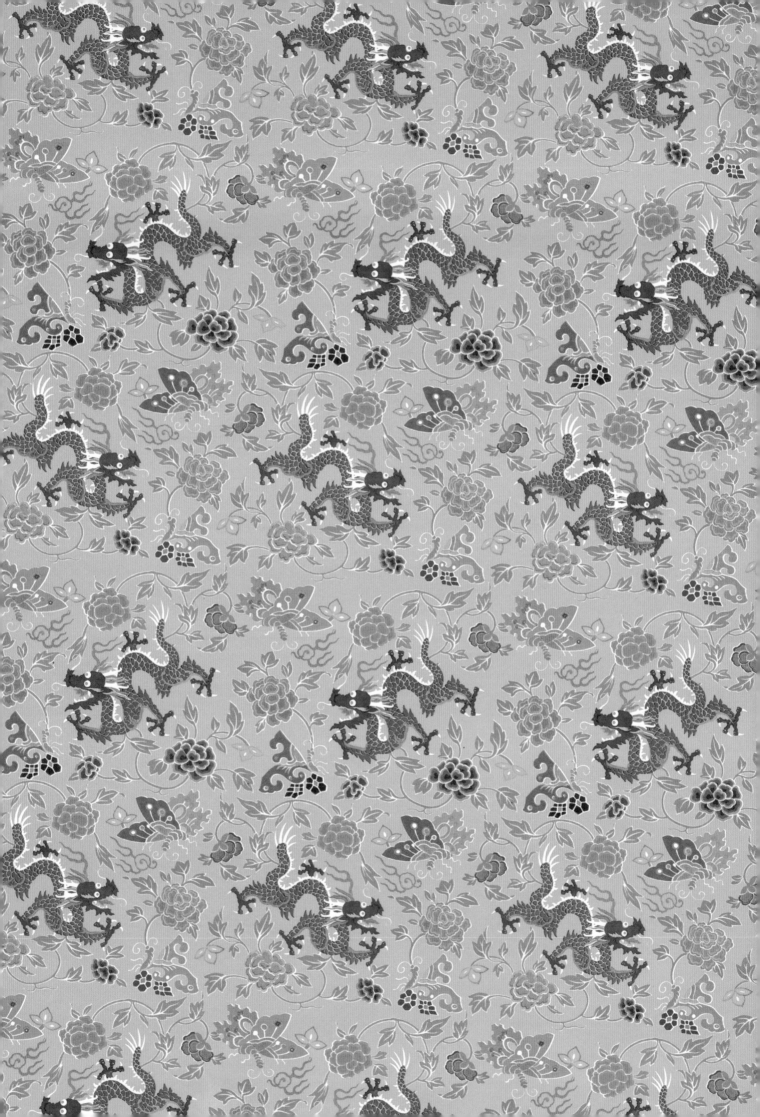

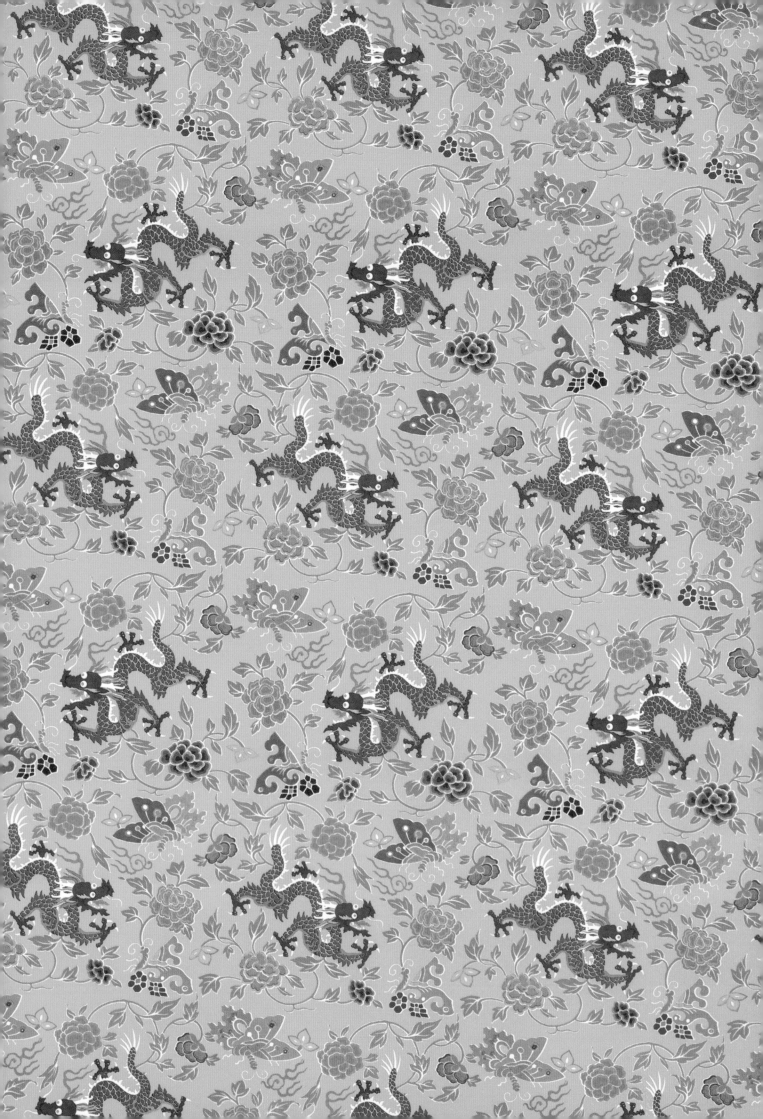

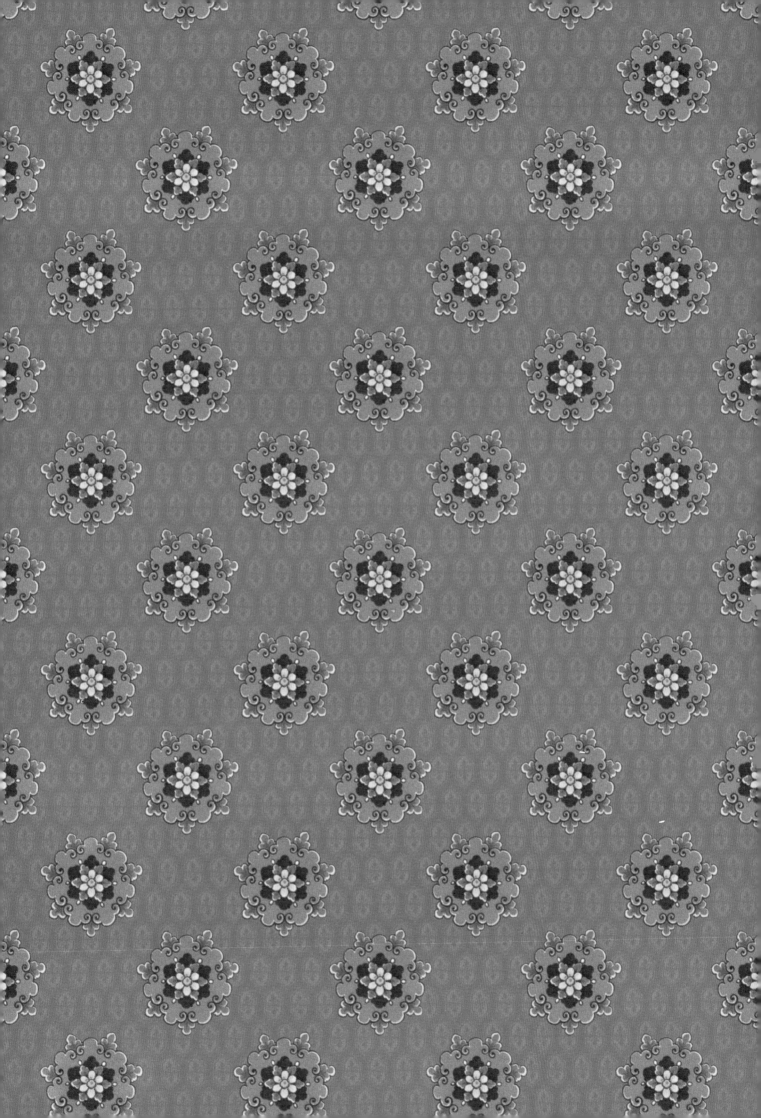

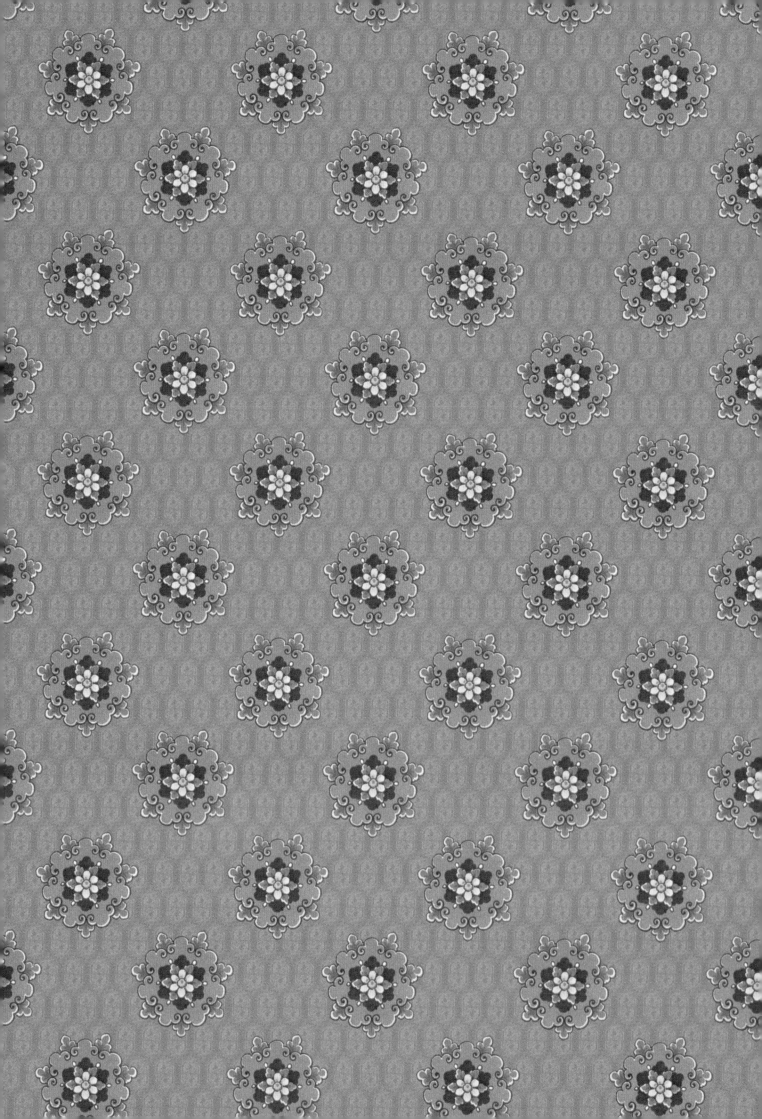

the Causes at Stafford on
Wednesday morning at 11 — 11
will be of importance to the
correspondence between him and
Mr P. can prove

I truly have a great desire to be in
Brighton if only to see my Cousin
has chosen to cut me entirely
have not heard from her since Christmas
why I know not, but the expence
Journey is so great and I feel sure
will do all in your power to get me
let. You state in your letter of
to that the Tenant of Grenville
is to pay, half at Midsummer

Carnarvon 22d July 1

dear Sir

received yours inclosing   £5. 6. 0 i
£5. 9. 0 therefore next quarter you
so good as to recollect the 3s for as
was your mistake and not mine
ought not to pay expences
never thanked you for your kindness
 using over Grenville Place for me but
have me I feel much indebted to you
your whole conduct towards me since

Brighton
who has ch
for I have m
and why I
of a journey
you will d
house let.
Manor Stea
Place is to
of his hou
to 2. 13. 3.
Amount you
as by your le
in October
there as a

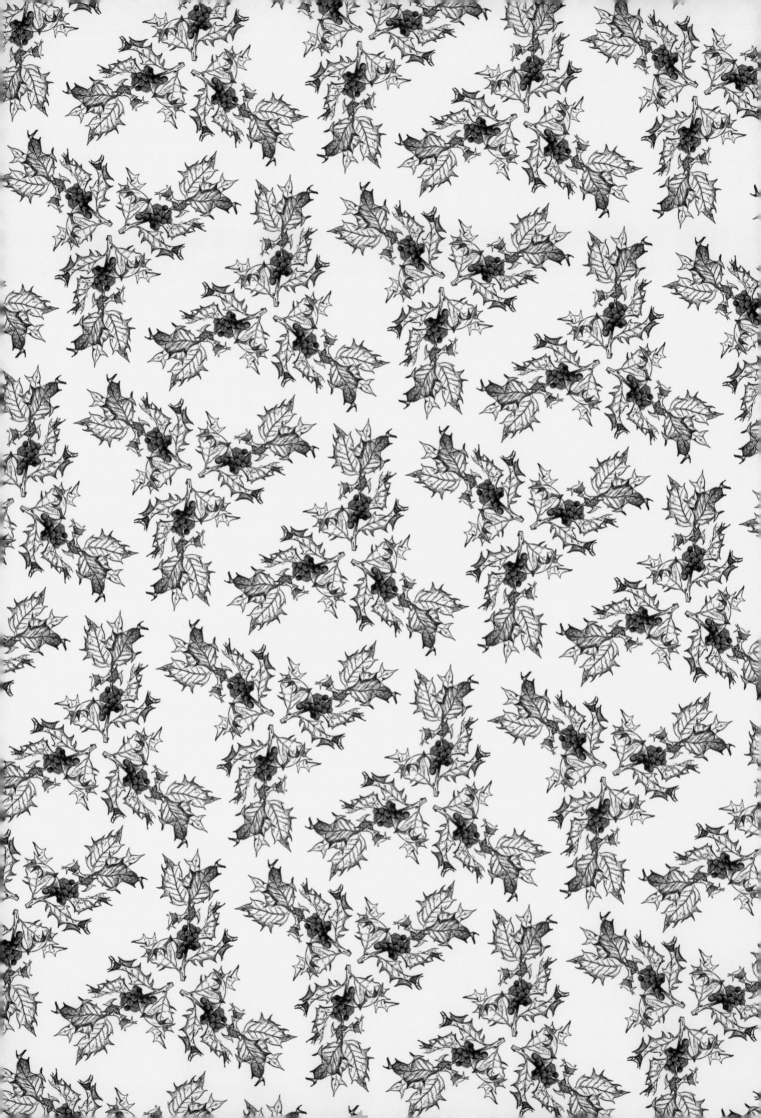